JUST  ONE ANSWER

JUST ONE ANSWER

Retold and Pictured by

John Faulkner

ALBERT WHITMAN & Company ·· Chicago

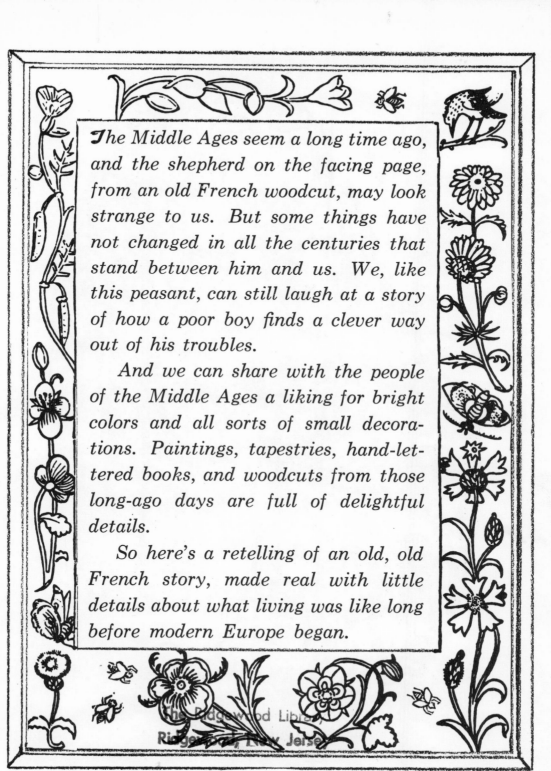

The Middle Ages seem a long time ago, and the shepherd on the facing page, from an old French woodcut, may look strange to us. But some things have not changed in all the centuries that stand between him and us. We, like this peasant, can still laugh at a story of how a poor boy finds a clever way out of his troubles.

And we can share with the people of the Middle Ages a liking for bright colors and all sorts of small decorations. Paintings, tapestries, hand-lettered books, and woodcuts from those long-ago days are full of delightful details.

So here's a retelling of an old, old French story, made real with little details about what living was like long before modern Europe began.

ONCE UPON A TIME there was a shepherd boy who had no better name than Sheepskin. Except for his dog he was quite alone in this world.

Now it happened that Sheepskin's old master died, and one way and another there was no place left for the boy.

"If I have nothing, nothing worries me," said Sheepskin. Calling his dog, he set off down the road to find a new master.

He soon came to a dark wood. It was a place
where robbers might wait to seize a traveler's purse.
Wolves might hide there, too. But Sheepskin was
not afraid. He had nothing to lose, and no wolf
with any pride would choose such a poor dinner.

By and by the road led out of the woods into the sunshine. Sheepskin began to see other travelers.

First came a man with a dancing bear. The boy stopped to stare. "That's how to live," he thought. "The man sings and the bear dances. But I can't sing and my dog can't dance."

A peasant jolted by in a two-wheeled cart.
"That's how to take to the road," Sheepskin said to
himself. "Let the horse get tired." And he stopped
to rest under a tree.

Soon two pilgrims passed. Their purses hung from their belts, and wide-brimmed hats shaded their eyes. One walked and carried a staff, the other rode a mule. "Who can find better company?" thought the boy, and he followed after the pilgrims.

The noonday sun shone down. Inside a high wall a church bell rang, calling the friars to their prayers.

"Now being a friar must be fine," Sheepskin told his dog. "Always a full stomach." But he had no head for prayers, and his feet had a way of dancing along.

In a field Sheepskin saw a plowman at work. His little son ran along beside the ox with a stick to urge the animal on. Sheepskin shook his head. He'd never be a plowman.

Across the fields came the sound of hunters. Their horses pranced and their bridles jingled. Each rider carried a hawk on his wrist.

Not far off was a town. Now Sheepskin saw a woman hurrying with a basket of eggs for the rich man's house. An old grandfather carried a load of firewood. No one paid any attention to Sheepskin. "Ah, well," he said. "They don't need us, and we don't need them."

In the town, the tavern door stood open.
Sheepskin felt in his purse for a penny. But since
he hadn't one when he started, he hadn't any now.
And his stomach was as empty as his purse.

A crafty old man saw Sheepskin standing in the street. Townspeople all said a penny turned black in this old man's purse before he spent it, he was so stingy. He was rich, too, with fields and cattle and sheep.

"Here's a good beginning," the old man thought. "I need a shepherd, and this is a likely looking boy with his dog."

The smell of bread baking in the town ovens made poor Sheepskin's mouth water. His dog's tongue hung out.

The crafty old man called, "Why do you stand there? Have you no work to do?"

Sheepskin stood on one foot and then the other. He could not find a word to say.

The old man shrugged. "It's no matter to me if you've run away," he said. "If you are a good lad, I can use you as a shepherd. Come along."

And so Sheepskin and his dog followed the man and were glad enough to share a bowl of soup and a piece of bread.

"You'll get five pieces of silver a year, food, and a place to sleep with my sheep," the old man said. "What more can you ask?"

With that, Sheepskin became the man's shepherd. He went out with the sheep each day. He kept a sharp lookout for wolves. Even on a market day he did not leave the flock.

The crafty old man treated Sheepskin just as he did his plowmen and his cowherd and his other workers. He gave him as little as possible and took as much work as he could get.

At night Sheepskin slept in the sheepfold. He always went to bed hungry. Even on a feast day there was never quite enough food to fill his stomach.

Now Sheepskin was not a clever boy—he'd never set the river on fire. But as time went on and he was always hungry, one idea began to fill his head. What a meal a fat lamb would make! By and by he could hardly look at a lamb without thinking of lamb chops and lamb stew and roast lamb.

But as quickly as Sheepskin's mouth began to water, his knees began to shake. If he took a lamb from the flock it would be a terrible crime. He'd be lucky to escape with nothing worse than a whipping.

Time went on, and things became worse. Even the pea soup was more water than anything else.

One day when Sheepskin looked in his leather bag all he found was a dry crust. His poor dog whined for a share.

When a boy's fat, he can laugh and sing. But when he's hungry, watch out! Then ideas can creep into the emptiest head.

It was too much! Sheepskin would not go hungry another day! That night he and his dog had a rich lamb stew and fell asleep with full stomachs.

Next morning Sheepskin trembled at what he had done. What would happen to him? But luck was with him, for twin lambs had been born during the night. No one was the wiser about Sheepskin's feast.

For many months Sheepskin put the idea of another fine meal out of his head. But his empty stomach kept reminding him. At last he could stand it no longer. Once again he and his dog ate like the lord of the manor.

But this time Sheepskin's luck failed him. The master counted his flock and found one lamb missing.

"Sheepskin!" he cried. "One lamb is gone!"

The boy thought of saying a wolf had stolen it. But the words would not come.

Seeing Sheepskin standing there, looking guilty, his master shouted, "Aha! You are a thief! Is this how you treat me when I have given you food and work? Wait, just wait! When court is next held under the ash tree, I will bring you before my lord's sheriff."

Still Sheepskin stood silent. He shook with fear and knew he was in trouble.

"You may be sure it will go hard with you," his master promised him.

And the old man went off, complaining about the way everyone tried to cheat him.

The milkmaid heard everything the master said. She told her mother, who was washing clothes at the river. Her mother told her sister who was busy with her spindle. In less time than it takes to put the cat out, everyone knew of Sheepskin's troubles.

That evening the man of law who lived in the town came to see Sheepskin.

"I hear your master is taking you to court," he said. "That's a serious matter."

Sheepskin agreed. By now he felt he'd be lucky to escape being hanged.

"I might be able to help you," the lawyer said. "Have you any money?"

Sheepskin went to his hiding place and took out five pieces of silver.

"That is just what my help will cost," said the lawyer. "And I am so sure you will go free that you can pay me later."

Could anyone help Sheepskin? He hardly dared think so, but he agreed to pay the silver. After all, what good would money be if he were hanged?

The lawyer said, "Now listen to me, Sheepskin. You must do just as I say. Everything depends on it."

Sheepskin never took his eyes off the lawyer.

"You must forget that you can say anything except one word. Just one word. Do you understand?"

Sheepskin nodded his head. For a moment the lawyer thought even one word might be too much for this shepherd boy. But he went on, "Whatever is asked, answer with this word and no other. Are you listening? No matter what it is, answer 'Baaa.' Now let's see if you understand."

Sheepskin opened and closed his mouth, but not a sound came out.

The lawyer said, "What is your name? Come on, the answer is—"

"Baaa!" bleated Sheepskin as if his life depended on it. And perhaps it did.

"Splendid!" cried the lawyer. "Who is your master?"

"Baaa!" answered Sheepskin.

"Perfect. Now that is all you are to say. Nothing more. Practice with your sheep. That one word will save you."

The day soon came when the sheriff held court. The cry went out for all the people to come.

First the sheriff heard the case of a woman who had not sent her meal to be ground at my lord's mill but had ground it herself. She had a fine to pay.

Next, a man was accused of taking a fish from my lord's stream. When he told how his sick wife had wanted a fish more than anything, he was let off with a warning.

Then it was poor Sheepskin's turn. His angry master clearly expected the boy to be punished. Why, hanging would be too good for him!

The sheriff said, "You are accused of stealing a lamb from your master. What is your name?"

Sheepskin was pushed to the front. He could hear the lawyer's advice—just one word, one word.

"Baaa!" Sheepskin exclaimed so loudly that he himself jumped.

The sheriff stared. "What did you say?"

"Baaa!" Sheepskin repeated, not so loudly.

The sheriff shook his head as if something were wrong with his ears.

"Now tell me," he said, "who is your master?"

Without a moment to think, Sheepskin said, "Baaa!" And in truth, that was the only thing he could say.

"This is an idiot!" cried the sheriff. "Any fool can hear that. Who accuses him?"

Sheepskin's master stepped forward. "I do. I accuse him of stealing a lamb from my flock."

"Think well," the sheriff told Sheepskin. "Did you take a lamb from the flock?"

"Baaa," declared Sheepskin.

People far back in the crowd began to wink at each other. Old men pulled their noses and looked wise.

"Baaa!" cried the sheriff. "Can you say nothing more?"

"Baaa," said Sheepskin meekly.

The sheriff was furious. No one ever behaved like this when he held court. Far off there was a tiny titter.

The sheriff frowned and everyone became silent. "I find," he said, "that no one but a fool would hire such a fool. A fool cannot be protected from his own foolishness. This poor shepherd is free."

The crafty old man cried for justice, but it did him no good. A peasant behind him whispered "Baaa!" and then one voice after the other repeated the hated sound.

But what of Sheepskin? When people told him how clever he was, what did he say? And when the lawyer ran up to demand his silver, what did the boy say?

Sheepskin had learned his lesson well. "Baaa!" he said, and whistled to his dog. Together they set off down the road from the town.